# CONTENTS

# Hurricane
# KATRINA

## The One We Feared

# INTRODUCTION

## Hurricane Basics

The ingredients for a hurricane include a pre-existing weather disturbance, warm tropical oceans, moisture, and relatively light winds aloft. If the right conditions persist long enough, they can combine to produce the violent winds, incredible waves, torrential rains, and floods we associate with this phenomenon.
Each year, an average of ten tropical storms develop over the Atlantic Ocean, Caribbean Sea, and Gulf of Mexico. Many of these remain over the ocean and never impact the U.S. coastline. Six of these storms become hurricanes each year. In an average 3-year period, roughly five hurricanes strike the US coastline, killing approximately 50 to 100 people anywhere from Texas to Maine. Of these, two are typically "major" or "intense" hurricanes (a category 3 or higher storm on the Saffir-Simpson Hurricane Scale).
What is a Hurricane? A hurricane is a type of tropical cyclone, which is a generic term for a low pressure system that generally forms in the tropics. The cyclone is accompanied by thunderstorms and, in the Northern Hemisphere, a counterclockwise circulation of winds near the earth's surface. Tropical cyclones are classified as follows:

* Sustained winds A 1-minute average wind measured at about 33 ft (10 meters) above the surface.
** 1 knot = 1 nautical mile per hour or 1.15 statute miles per hour. Abbreviated as "kt".

**Tropical Depression** - An organized system of clouds and thunderstorms with a defined surface circulation and maximum sustained winds* of 38 mph (33 kt**) or less.

**Tropical Storm** - An organized system of strong thunderstorms with a defined surface circulation and maximum sustained winds of 39-73 mph (34-63 kt)

**Hurricane** - An intense tropical weather system of strong thunderstorms with a well-defined surface circulation and maximum sustained winds of 74 mph (64 kt) or higher.

Hurricanes are categorized according to the strength of their winds using the Saffir-Simpson Hurricane Scale. A Category 1 storm has the lowest wind speeds, while a Category 5 hurricane has the strongest. These are relative terms, because lower category storms can sometimes inflict greater damage than higher category storms, depending on where they strike and the particular hazards they bring. In fact tropical storms can also produce significant damage and loss of life, mainly due to flooding.

## The Saffir-Simpson Hurricane Scale

The Saffir-Simpson Hurricane Scale is a 1-5 rating based on the hurricane's present intensity. This is used to give an estimate of the potential property damage and flooding expected along the coast from a hurricane landfall. Wind speed is the determining factor in the scale, as storm surge values are highly dependent on the slope of the continental shelf and the shape of the coastline, in the landfall region. Note that all winds are using the U.S. 1-minute average.

### Category One Hurricane:
Winds 74-95 mph (64-82 kt or 119-153 km/hr). Storm surge generally 4-5 ft above normal. No real damage to building structures. Damage primarily to unanchored mobile homes, shrubbery, and trees. Some damage to poorly constructed signs, some coastal road flooding and minor pier damage. Hurricane Lili of 2002 made landfall on the Louisiana coast as a Category One hurricane. Hurricane Gaston of 2004 was a Category One hurricane that made landfall along the central South Carolina coast.

**Category Two Hurricane:**
Winds 96-110 mph (83-95 kt or 154-177 km/hr). Storm surge generally 6-8 feet above normal. Some roofing material, door, and window damage of buildings. Considerable damage to shrubbery and trees with some trees blown down. Considerable damage to mobile homes, poorly constructed signs, and piers. Coastal and low-lying escape routes flood 2-4 hours before arrival of the hurricane center. Small craft in unprotected anchorages break moorings. Hurricane Frances of 2004 made landfall over the southern end of Hutchinson Island, Florida as a Category Two hurricane. Hurricane Isabel of 2003 made landfall near Drum Inlet on the Outer Banks of North Carolina as a Category 2 hurricane.

**Category Three Hurricane:**
Winds 111-130 mph (96-113 kt or 178-209 km/hr). Storm surge generally 9-12 ft above normal. Some structural damage to small residences and utility buildings with a minor amount of curtainwall failures. Damage to shrubbery and trees with foliage blown off trees and large trees blown down. Mobile homes and poorly constructed signs are destroyed. Low-lying escape routes are cut by rising water 3-5 hours before arrival of the center of the hurricane. Flooding near the coast destroys smaller structures with larger structures damaged by battering from floating debris. Terrain continuously lower than 5 ft above mean sea level may be flooded inland 8 miles (13 km) or more. Evacuation of low-lying residences with several blocks of the shoreline may be required. Hurricanes Jeanne and Ivan of 2004 were Category Three hurricanes when they made landfall in Florida and in Alabama, respectively.

**Category Four Hurricane:**
Winds 131-155 mph (114-135 kt or 210-249 km/hr). Storm surge generally 13-18 ft above normal. More extensive curtainwall failures with some complete roof structure failures on small residences. Shrubs, trees, and all signs are blown down. Complete destruction of mobile homes. Extensive damage to doors and windows. Low-lying escape routes may be cut by rising water 3-5 hours before arrival of the center of the hurricane. Major damage to lower floors of structures near the shore. Terrain lower than 10 ft above sea level may be flooded requiring massive evacuation of residential areas as far inland as 6 miles (10 km). Hurricane Charley of 2004 was a Category Four hurricane made landfall in Charlotte County, Florida with winds of 150 mph. Hurricane Dennis of 2005 struck the island of Cuba as a Category Four hurricane.

**Category Five Hurricane:**
Winds greater than 155 mph (135 kt or 249 km/hr). Storm surge generally greater than 18 ft above normal. Complete roof failure on many residences and industrial buildings. Some complete building failures with small utility buildings blown over or away. All shrubs, trees, and signs blown down. Complete destruction of mobile homes. Severe and extensive window and door damage. Low-lying escape routes are cut by rising water 3-5 hours before arrival of the center of the hurricane. Major damage to lower floors of all structures located less than 15 ft above sea level and within 500 yards of the shoreline. Massive evacuation of residential areas on low ground within 5-10 miles (8-16 km) of the shoreline may be required. Only 3 Category Five Hurricanes have made landfall in the United States since records began: The Labor Day Hurricane of 1935, Hurricane Camille (1969), and Hurricane Andrew in August, 1992. The 1935 Labor Day Hurricane struck the Florida Keys with a minimum pressure of 892 mb--the lowest pressure ever observed in the United States. Hurricane Camille struck the Mississippi Gulf Coast causing a 25-foot storm surge, which inundated Pass Christian. Hurricane Andrew of 1992 made landfall over southern Miami-Dade County, Florida causing 26.5 billion dollars in losses--the costliest hurricane on record. In addition, Hurricane Gilbert of 1988 was a Category Five hurricane at peak intensity and is the strongest Atlantic tropical cyclone on record with a minimum pressure of 888 mb.

## Overview of Hurricane Katrina

Hurricane Katrina was one of the strongest storms to impact the coast of the United States during the last 100 years. With sustained winds during landfall of 140 mph (a strong category 4 hurricane on the Saffir-Simpson scale) and minimum central pressure the third lowest on record at landfall (920 mb), Katrina caused widespread devastation along the central Gulf Coast states of the US. Cities such as New Orleans, LA, Mobile, AL, and Gulfport, MS bore the brunt of Katrina's force and will need weeks and months of recovery efforts to restore normality. Other storms have had stronger sustained winds when they made landfall including the following:
The Labor Day Hurricane, Florida Keys, September 2, 1935, Category 5, 892 mb, Approaching 200 mph, Hurricane Camille, Mississippi, August 17, 1969, Category 5, 909 mb, Approaching 190 mph, Hurricane

Andrew, Southeast Florida, August 24, 1992, Category 5, 922 mb, 165 mph, Hurricane Charley, Punta Gorda, Florida, August 13, 2004, Category 4, 941 mb, 150 mph.
The most deadly hurricane to strike the U.S. made landfall in Galveston, Texas on September 8, 1900. This was also the greatest natural disaster to ever strike the U.S., claiming more than 8000 lives when the storm surge caught the residents of this island city by surprise.

Hurricane Katrina developed initially as a tropical depression (TD #12 of the season) in the southeastern Bahamas on August 23rd. This tropical depression strengthened into Tropical Storm Katrina the next day. It then moved slowly along a northwesterly then westerly track through the Bahamas, increasing in strength during this time. A few hours before landfall in south Florida at around 6.30 EDT on August 25th, Katrina strengthened to become a category 1 (windspeeds of 75mph or greater) hurricane. Landfall occurred between Hallandale Beach and North Miami Beach, Florida, with windspeeds of approximately 80 mph. Gusts of above 90 mph were measured as Katrina came ashore. As the storm moved southwest across the tip of the Florida peninsula, Katrina's winds decreased slightly before regaining hurricane strength in the Gulf of Mexico. Given that Katrina spent only seven hours over land, its strength was not significantly diminished and it quickly re-intensified shortly after moving over the warm waters of the Gulf.
Katrina moved almost due westward after entering the Gulf of Mexico. A mid-level ridge centered over Texas weakened and moved westward allowing Katrina to gradually turn to the northwest and then north into the weakness in the ridging over the days that followed. Atmospheric and sea-surface conditions (an upper level anticyclone over the Gulf and warm SSTs) were conducive to cyclone's rapid intensification, which lead to Katrina attaining 'major hurricane' status on the afternoon of the 26th.

Continuing to strengthen and move northwards during the next 48 hours, Katrina reached maximum windspeeds on the morning of Sunday August 28th of 150 kts (category 5), and its minimum central pressure dropped that afternoon to 902 mb - the 4th lowest on record for an Atlantic storm. Although Katrina, at its peak strength was comparable to Camille's intensity, it was a significantly larger storm and impacted a broader area of the Gulf coast. Although tropical cyclones of category 5 strength are rarely sustained for long durations (due to internal dynamics), Katrina remained a strong category 4 strength hurricane despite the entrainment of dryer air and an opening of the eyewall to the south and southwest before landfall on the morning of the 29th. Landfalling windspeeds at Grand Isle, LA were approximately 140 mph with a central pressure of 920mb - the 3rd lowest on record for a landfalling Atlantic storm in the US.

Satellite imagery of Hurricane Katrina as it moves through the Gulf of Mexico and makes landfall in Louisiana.
*courtesy of NOAA/Satellite and Information Service*

Below is a synopsis of the conditions that produced historic Hurricane Katrina, as well as some information of rain and wind records and a very preliminary description of the major impacts.

## Rain, Wind, Storm Surge

Eastern Florida: During its initial landfall in southern Florida, Katrina generated over 5 inches of rainfall across a large area of southeastern Florida. An analysis by NOAA's Climate Prediction Center shows that parts of the region received heavy rainfall, over 15 inches in some locations, which caused localized flooding. Winds at landfall north of Miami were 80 mph (category 1 strength), leading to some damage and extensive power outages.

Gulf Coast: Rainfall from Katrina's outer bands began affecting the Gulf coast well before landfall. As Katrina came ashore on August 29th, rainfall exceeded rates of 1 inch/hour across a large area of the coast. NOAA's Climate Reference Network Station in Newton, MS (60 miles east of Jackson, MS) measured rainfall rates of over an inch an hour for 3 consecutive hours, with rates of over 0.5 in/hr for 5 hours during August 29th. Precipitation analysis from NOAA's Climate Prediction Center show that rainfall accumulations exceeded 8-10 inches along much of the hurricane's path and to the east of the track. Windspeeds over 140 mph were recorded at landfall in southeastern Louisiana while winds gusted to over 100 mph in New Orleans, just west of the eye. As the hurricane made its second landfall on the Mississippi/Louisiana border, windspeeds were approximately 110 kts (125 mph). Gusts of over 80mph were recorded in Mobile and 90 mph in Biloxi, MS. The central pressure at landfall was 920 mb, which ranked 3rd lowest on record for US-landfalling storms behind Camille (909 mb) and the Labor Day hurricane that struck the Florida Keys in 1935 (892 mb). Hurricane Andrew in 1992 dropped to fourth, as its central pressure was 922 mb at landfall. Katrina also reached a minimum central pressure of 902 mb at its peak, ranking 4th lowest on record for all Atlantic basin hurricanes.

Inland: As the storm moved inland and weakened to a tropical storm on the 29th, rainfall became the primary impact. Rainfall amounts exceeded 2-4 inches across a large area from the Gulf coast to the Ohio Valley. As a result, flood watches and warnings were common across these regions. Rain bands from Katrina also produced tornadoes causing further damage in areas such as Georgia.

## IMPACTS

LOSS OF LIFE: From the Gulf states (principally Louisiana and Mississippi), the loss of life is unknown but will likely reach well into the hundreds and possibly higher. It is clearly one of the most devastating natural disasters in recent US history. From Katrina's first landfall in Florida, while it was at category one strength, initial estimates suggest 11 deaths resulted.

FLOODING: The loss of life and property damage was worsened by breaks in the levees that separate New Orleans from surrounding lakes. At least 80% of New Orleans was under flood water on August 31st, largely as a result of levee failures from Lake Pontchartrain. The combination of strong winds, heavy rainfall and storm surge led to breaks in the earthen levee after the storm passed, leaving some parts of New Orleans under 20 feet of water. Storm surge from Mobile Bay led to inundation of Mobile, Alabama causing imposition of a dusk-to-dawn curfew for the City. Large portions of Biloxi and Gulfport, Mississippi were underwater as a result of a 20 to 30+ foot storm surge which flooded the cities.

OIL INDUSTRY: A major economic impact for the nation was the disruption to the oil industry from Katrina. Preliminary estimates from the Mineral Management Service suggest that oil production in the Gulf of Mexico was reduced by 1.4 million barrels per day (or 95 % of the daily Gulf of Mexico production) as a result of the hurricane. Gasoline had reached a record high price/gallon as of Monday August 30th with concerns over refinery capacity apparently driving the increase. More information is available from a Department of Energy report.

POWER OUTAGES: Over 1.7 million people lost power as a result of the storm in the Gulf states, with power companies estimating that it will take more than several weeks to restore power to some locations. Drinking water was also unavailable in New Orleans due to a broken water main that serves the city. Power was lost to 1.3 million customers in southeastern Florida from the initial landfall on August 24th.

COST: Estimates for insured damages for Hurricane Katrina are still extremely preliminary and properly assessing losses will take weeks or months. However, the cost of Katrina will certainly be a minimum of several billion dollars and might exceed losses from Hurricane Andrew. Andrew caused $15.5 billion in insured damage in 1992. Adjusted for inflation, Andrew resulted in more than $25 billion in insured damage.

TRAVEL: Both of New Orleans' airports were flooded and closed on August 30th and bridges of Interstate 10 leading east out of the city were destroyed. Most of the coastal highways along the Gulf were impassable in places and most minor roads near the shore were still underwater or covered in debris as of August 30th. Katrina also disrupted travel as it headed inland, with more than 2 inches of rain falling across a large area from the coast to parts of Ohio during the 48 hours after Katrina made landfall.

1

*courtesy of DigitalGlobe*

**1:** Satellite image of Biloxi, MS before Hurricane Katrina.

**2:** Satellite image of Biloxi, MS after the devastating force of Hurricane Katrina.

2

*courtesy of DigitalGlobe*

*courtesy of DigitalGlobe*

**3:** Satellite image of New Orleans, LA before Hurricane Katrina made landfall.

**4:** Satellite image of New Orleans, LA after Hurricane Katrina's destructive blow.

*courtesy of DigitalGlobe*

# FLORIDA

A few hours before landfall in south Florida at around 6:30 EDT on August 25, Katrina strengthened to become a category 1 (windspeeds of 75 mph or greater) hurricane. Landfall occurred between Hallandale Beach and North Miami Beach, with windspeeds of approximately 80 mph. As the storm moved southwest across the tip of Florida peninsula, Katrina's winds decreased slightly before regaining hurricane strength in the Gulf of Mexico. Because Katrina passed over Florida in 7 hours, its strength was not significantly diminished before moving over the warm waters of the Gulf.

**5**

AP Photo/J. Pat Carter

*AP Photo/J. Pat Carter*

**6**

*AP Photo/Luis M. Alvarez*

**7**

**5:** Sand is blown off the beach at Fort Lauderdale, Fla. late Thursday, Aug. 25, 2005 as Hurricane Katrina came ashore. Hurricane Katrina dumped sheets of rain, kicked up the surf and blew strong winds ashore Thursday, toppling trees and driving sand across waterfront streets as it made landfall on the state's densely populated southeast coast.

**6:** A Miami Dade police car sits in the middle of a flooded Princeton, Fla. street Friday, Aug. 26, 2005 after Hurricane Katrina dumped several inches of rain on south Florida.

**7:** A family stands on the doorstep of their home Friday, Aug. 26, 2005, in Florida City, Fla. Hurricane Katrina flooded streets, darkened homes and felled trees as it plowed across South Florida before emerging over the Gulf of Mexico.

**8:** This photo made available by Miami-Dade Fire Rescue shows an overpass under construction in Miami-Dade County which collapsed onto State Road 836 Friday Aug. 26, 2005. Hurricane Katrina caused localized flooding, down trees and over a million homes without power.

**9:** Noe Morua pushes his bike past a flooded mobile home park in Homestead, Fla., Friday, Aug. 26, 2005. Hurricane Katrina flooded streets, darkened homes and felled trees as it plowed across South Florida before emerging over the Gulf of Mexico.

**10:** Sloppy Joe's Bar in Key West, Fla., is a popular "watering hole" to escape the rain and wind of Hurricane Katrina on Friday, Aug. 26, 2005. Utility crews scrambled to restore power to more than 1 million customers Friday as Katrina, blamed for seven deaths and miles of flooded streets in South Florida, threatened the state with an encore visit.

10

# LOUISIANA

In the Gulf of Mexico, atmospheric and sea-surface conditions were conducive to the storm's rapid intensification, which lead to Katrina attaining 'major hurricane' status on the afternoon of the 26th. Over the 48 hours the storm was in the Gulf, Katrina reached maximum windspeeds on the morning of August 28 — 150 kts or 172 mph. Its minimum central pressure dipped that afternoon to 902 mb — the 4th lowest on record for an Atlantic storm. Although Katrina, at its peak strength was comparable to Camille's intensity, it was a significantly larger storm and impacted a broader area of the Gulf Coast. At 6:10am CDT on August 29, Katrina made landfall at Grand Isle, LA, with speeds at approximately 140 mph with a central pressure of 920mb — the 3rd lowest on record for an Atlantic storm in the US. (Category 4) Continuing Northward . . . Katrina made a second landfall near the Louisiana/Mississippi border at 10:00 am CDT with maximum winds of near 125 mph (Category 3)

11

**11:** Louisiana Gov. Kathleen Blanco, center, flanked by New Orleans Mayor Ray Nagin, left, and Couniclman Oliver Thomas, speaks during a news conference on Hurricane Katrina at New Orleans City Hall, Saturday, Aug. 27, 2005.

**12:** Vehicles leave New Orleans ahead of Hurricane Katrina on Sunday, Aug. 28, 2005. The Category 5 storm made landfall on Monday.

**13:** Floodwaters from Hurricane Katrina flow over a levee along Inner Harbor Navigaional Canal near downtown New Orleans Tuesday, Aug. 30, 2005. Hurricane Katrina did extensive damage when it made landfall on Monday.

AP Photo/Bill Haber

AP Photo/David J. Phillip

**14:** Bryan Vernon and Dorothy Bell are rescued from their rooftop after Hurricane Katrina hit, causing flooding in their New Orleans neighborhood, Monday Morning, Aug. 29, 2005. Officials called for a mandatory evacuation of the city, but many residents remained in the city.

**15:** Some of the thousands of displaced residents take cover from Hurricane Katrina at the Superdome, a last-resort shelter, in New Orleans about midnight, Sunday, Aug. 28, 2005. Officials called for a mandatory evacuation of the city, but many residents remained in the city.

**16:** The Louisiana Superdome, shown in this aerial view, was damaged by Hurricane Katrina and sits surrounded by floodwaters Tuesday, Aug. 30, 2005 in New Orleans.

**17:** Emanuel Honeycutt is followed by his son Emanuel Jr., 11, as he carries his daughter Eman, 9, through floodwaters in the French Quarter in New Orleans, Tuesday, Aug. 30, 2005, after the area was hit by Hurricane Katrina. Officials called for a mandatory evacuation of the city, but many residents remained in the city.

**18:** A boat sits on a house damaged by Hurricane Katrina Tuesday, Aug. 30, 2005 in Slidell, La.

17

*AP Photo/Eric Gay*

18

*AP Photo/Eric Gay*

AP Photo/Dave Martin

**19:** Thousands of New Orleans residents gather at an evacuation staging area along Interstate-10 in Metairie, La., on Thursday, Sept. 1, 2005. The residents were either evacuated by air or walked to the Interstate to escape the city still besieged by flooding and no electricity.

**20:** Prisoners from the Orleans Parish Prison are staged on the highway as floodwaters from Hurricane Katrina cover the streets Tuesday, Aug. 30, 2005 in downtown New Orleans.

AP Photo/David J. Phillip

**21**

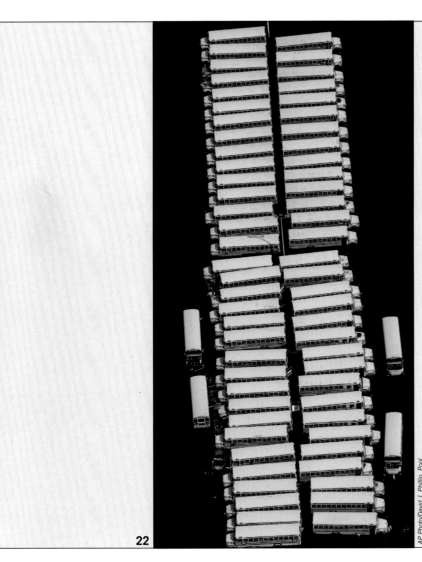

**22**

**21:** New Orleans Police and volunteers use boats to rescue residents from a flooded neighborhood on the east side of New Orleans, Wednesday, Aug. 31, 2005. Hurricane Katrina left much of the city under water. Officials called for a mandatory evacuation of the city, but many residents remained in the city and had to be rescued from flooded homes and hotels.

**22:** School buses remain surrounded by floodwaters in the aftermath of Hurricane Katrina Saturday, Sept. 10, 2005 in New Orleans.

AP Photo/Eric Gay

**23**

**23:** Looters make off with merchandise from several downtown businesses in New Orleans, Tuesday, Aug. 30, 2005, after Hurricane Katrina hit the area.

**24:** A home surrounded by floodwaters from Hurricane Katrina burns Friday, Sept. 2, 2005 in New Orleans.

**25:** Boats damaged by Hurricane Katrina are stacked on top of one another Tuesday, Aug. 30, 2005 in New Orleans.

AP Photo/David J. Phillip

**24**

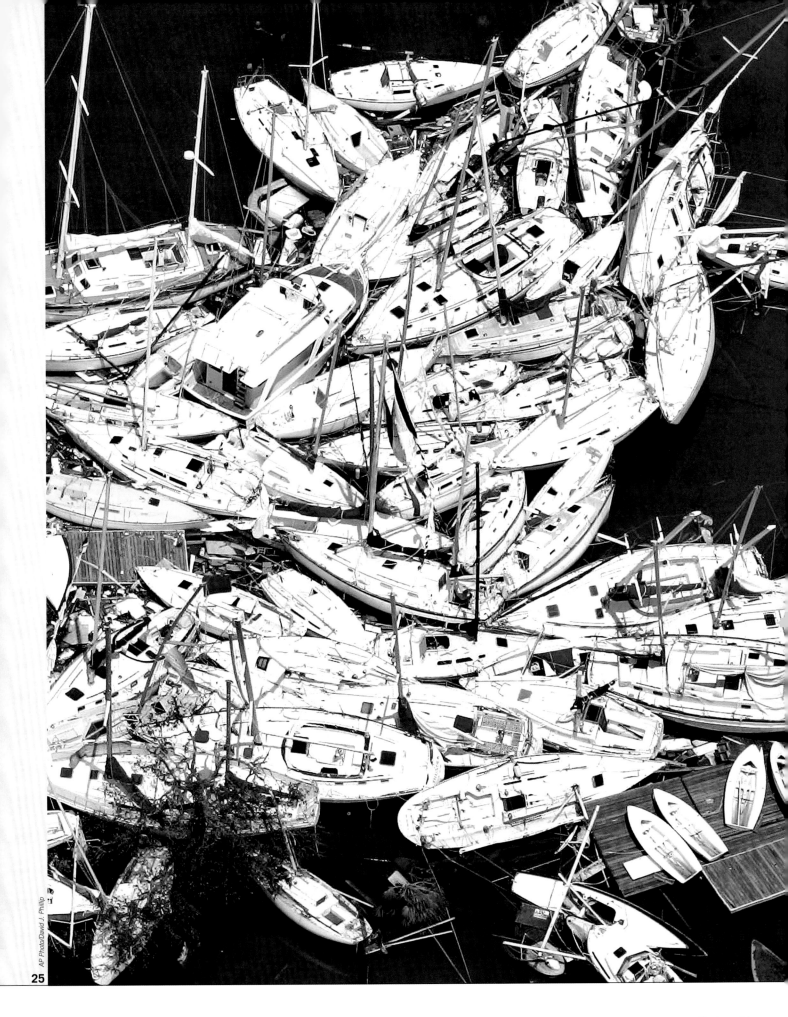

25

**26:** A U.S. Military convoy drives through floodwaters from Hurricane Katrina in downtown New Orleans Friday, Sept. 2, 2005.

**27:** Floodwaters from Hurricane Katrina pour through a levee along Inner Harbor Navigaional Canal near downtown New Orleans, La., Tuesday, Aug. 30, 2005, a day after Katrina passed through the city.

26

*AP Photo/David J. Phillip*

27

*AP Photo/Vincent Laforet, Pool*

AP Photo/Phil Coale

**28:** Victims of Hurricane Katrina are shown outside the Louisiana Superdome as they wait for evacuation, Thursday, Sept. 1, 2005, in New Orleans, LA.

**29:** Milvertha Hendricks, 84, center waits in the rain with other flood victims outside the convention center in New Orleans, Thursday, Sept. 1, 2005. Officials called for a mandatory evacuation of the city, but many residents remained in the city and had to be rescued from flooded homes and hotels and remain in the city awaiting a way out.

AP Photo/Susan Walsh

31

AP Photo/David J. Phillip

**30:** A soldier patrols the street next to a house fire in the Garden District in New Orleans, Tuesday Sept. 6, 2005. Fires continued to break out across the flood besieged city that had little running water causing a fierce challenge for the New Orleans Fire Dept.

**31:** Residents are rescued by helicopter from the floodwaters of Hurricane Katrina Thursday, Sept. 1, 2005 in New Orleans.

**32:** A victim of Hurricane Katrina is lifted into a rescue helicopter from a church located in one of the flooded neighborhoods north of New Orleans, LA, Sunday, Sept. 4, 2005.

32

AP Photo/Phil Coale

**33**

**34**

**33:** This image released by FEMA Friday Sept. 2, 2005 shows A Red Cross volunteer comforting a hurricane victim in the Houston Asrodome Friday Sept. 2, 2005. Approximately 18,000 hurricane Katrina survivors were temporarily sheltered in the Red Cross shelter at the Astrodome and Reliant center.

**34:** Daniel Hoffmeier, right, with the Coast Guard, along with an unidentified police officer, helps load children into a helicopter while transporting victims of Hurricane Katrina from the Ernest N. Morial Convention Center to the airport, Saturday Sept. 3, 2005 in New Orleans, La..

**35:** Search and rescue personal go house to house through the floodwaters of Hurricane Katrina Wednesday, Sept. 7, 2005 in New Orleans.

**36:** Leonard Thomas, 23, cries after a SWAT team burst into the flooded home he and his family were living in on Monday, Sept. 5, 2005 in New Orleans, La. Neighbors had reported that they were squatting in the house in the wake of Hurricane Katrina but the authorities left after his family proved they owned the house. Some rescuers were not taking any more food and water to those who have decided to stay in an effort to force them out.

35

AP Photo/David J. Phillip, Pool

36

AP Photo/Rick Bowmer

**37**

*AP Photo/David J. Phillip, Pool*

**37:** As floodwaters from Hurricane Katrina receed, a layer of mud covers the streets and homes Thursday, Sept. 8, 2005 in St. Bernard Parish near New Orleans.

**38:** Medical technician USAF Sgt. Bret Owen of Choctaw, OK gives aid to Hurricane Katrina victims at a temporary hospital set up at the New Orleans airport on Saturday, Sept. 3, 2005.

**39:** A military helicopter drops sandbags to repair a broken levee, Tuesday, Sept. 6, 2005, in New Orleans.

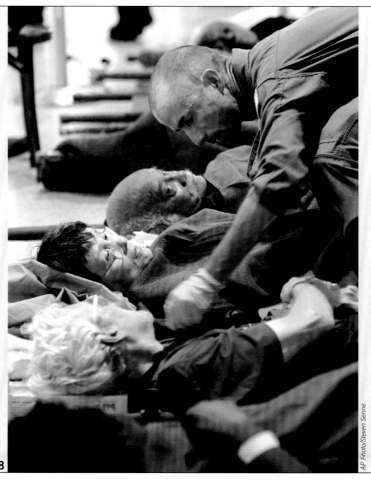

**38**

*AP Photo/Steven Senne*

39

41

AP Photo/Susan Walsh, File

42

AP Photo/Rick Bowmer

**40:** A small dog is leashed by a rescuer in New Orleans on Wednesday, Sept. 7, 2005. Thousands of animals were stranded and separated from their owners in the wake of Hurricane Katrina which devastated the area.

**41:** Marine One with President Bush aboard, flies over areas of Louisiana devastated by Hurricane Katrina Sept. 2, 2005. Analysts inside and outside the government agree that the $62 billion the federal government has spent so far is merely the first installment. The government has never dealt with a disaster that affected 90,000 square miles of the Gulf Coast, displaced hundreds of thousands of people and left an entire metropolitan area under water.

**42:** Rescue workers move along Peoples Avenue in an air boat in New Orleans on Saturday, Sept. 10, 2005. Efforts continued to locate bodies and survivors of Hurricane Katrina, 12 days after it hit the Gulf Coast.

**43:** A row of buses make their way to the Superdome to remove victims of Hurricane Katrina in New Orleans, La., Sept. 2, 2005. Hundreds of people were rescued from their homes as the city continued to face rising flood waters.

**44:** Thousand of people displaced by Hurricane Katrina await buses to depart the Superdome in New Orleans, Louisiana, Sept. 2, 2005. Analysts inside and outside the government agree that the $62 billion the federal government has spent so far is merely the first installment. The government has never dealt with a disaster that affected 90,000 square miles of the Gulf Coast, displaced hundreds of thousands of people and left an entire metropolitan area under water.

**45:** This satellite image provided by DigitalGlobe shows an overview of downtown New Orleans Wednesday Aug. 31, 2005. The Superdome can be seen in the lower left hand corner; the Mississippi River is in the lower right hand corner; and Lake Pontchartrain can be seen at the top of the image. Flooded streets can be seen throughout the image

*AP Photo/Robert Galbraith, Pool*

*AP Photo/Robert Galbraith/Pool*

45

**46:** Floodwaters from Hurricane Katrina continue to receed near downtown New Orleans Sunday, Sept. 11, 2005.

**47:** Flood victims are seen among their belongings and trash by the Superdome in the aftermath of Hurricane Katrina Sept. 3, 2005, in New Orleans, La.

48

**48:** Ted Mack sits outside a bar on Bourbon Street in the historic French Quarter in New Orleans, La., Tuesday Sept. 6, 2005. Some bars were open in the French Quarter despite efforts by city and national authorities to completely evacuate the flood besieged city.

**49:** Firefighters from New Orleans and other cities around the country work a fire at an office building in New Orleans on Thursday, Sept. 15, 2005. With electrical systems soaked, and gas leaks a possibility, fire officials were answering calls in force as the city attempted to return to a sense of normalcy.

49

AP Photo/Dave Martin

**51**

**50:** A tattered U.S. flag flies in front of the Hyatt, in New Orleans, in this Aug. 29, 2005 file photo, where dozens of windows were blown out when Hurricane Katrina made land fall. Getting hotels operating again will be crucial to the city's rebuilding efforts, as tourism is New Orleans' number two industry.

**51:** A makeshift tomb at a New Orleans street corner conceals a body that had been lying on the sidewalk for days in the wake of Hurricane Katrina on Sunday, Sept. 4, 2005.

**52:** Workers man giant pumps on the 17th Street levy along Lake Pontchartrain in New Orleans on Wednesday, Sept. 14, 2005. Georgia Gov. Sonny Perdue and Maj. Gen. David Poythress, Georgia's adjutant general, toured the area and visited with Georgia National Guard troops who are helping in recovery efforts from Hurricane Katrina.

AP Photo/Ric Feld

**52**

**53**

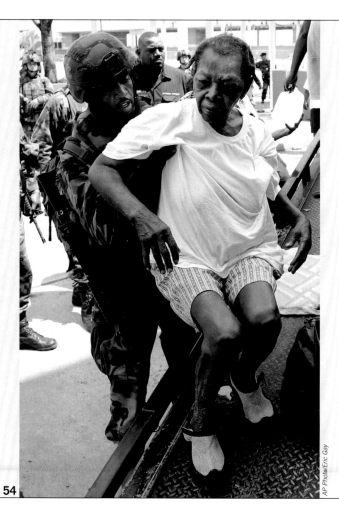

**54**

**53:** Hurricane Katrina victim Nita LaGarde, 89, holds hands with Tanisha Blevin, 5, as they are evacuated from the convention center to a helicopter in New Orleans, La., Saturday, Sept. 3, 2005. After days of waiting, hundreds of people were evacuated from the city by bus and helicopter.

**54:** Military troops aid a truck load of elderly victims of Hurricane Katrina outside the Convention Center in the besieged city of New Orleans on Friday, Sept. 2, 2005. A huge military presence had arrived in the city, restoring order and bringing with them food and water to feed the thousands of victims of Hurricane Katrina.

**55:** Floodwaters from Hurricane Katrina cover a portion of New Orleans, La., Tuesday, Aug. 30, 2005, a day after Katrina passed through the city.

**56:** A military C-130 plane sprays pesticide over still flooded parts of New Orleans, Louisiana Tuesday, Sept. 13, 2005. Hurricane Katrina hit the region on August 29 causing numerous deaths and severe property damage in Louisiana and Mississippi.

55

*AP Photo/David J. Phillip*

56

*AP Photo/Brian Snyder, Pool*

57

58

59

**57:** An historic America Flag is moved aside to allow people to see the markings that indicated the house was searched in New Orleans Saturday Sept. 17, 2005. Each house is being searched looking for victims of Hurricane Katrina.

**58:** The floor of Houston's Astrodome is covered with cots and evacuees from hurricane ravaged New Orleans Friday, Sept. 2, 2005. Texas opened two more giant centers for victims of Hurricane Katrina on Friday after refugees filled Houston's Astrodome to capacity.

**59:** Texas Gov. Rick Perry, right, is embraced by an unidentifed Hurricane Katrina evacuee as he meets with evacuees at a shelter on Monday, Sept. 5, 2005, in Austin, Texas. The state delivered social services to Hurricane Katrina evacuees in Texas as 240,000 refugees started to make their home in the state.

**60:** Sunset is seen over New Orleans September 12, 2005. U.S. President George W. Bush, on a tour of devastated New Orleans on Monday, rejected charges the government was slow to respond to Hurricane Katrina because most of the victims were black or because the nation's military was over-extended in Iraq. Hurricane Katrina hit the region on August 29 causing numerous deaths and severe property damage in Louisiana and Mississippi.

60

# MISSISSIPPI

Katrina made landfall at the Louisiana/Mississippi border at 10:00 am, August 29, with winds of near 125 mph. (Category 3). Bay St. Louis, Pass Christian, Gulfport and Biloxi were directly in path of storm. Traveling inland to the north/northeast, Katrina remained a hurricane until reaching Laurel, MS, when it weakened and became a tropical depression when it reached Tennessee on August 30.

61

AP Photo/David J. Phillip

**61:** From an aerial view a bulldozer clears debris from Hurricane Katrina Wednesday, Aug. 31, 2005, in Long Beach, Miss.

**62:** Waves crash against a boat washed onto Highway 90 as Hurricane Katrina hit the Gulf Coast Monday, Aug. 29, 2005 in Gulfport, Miss.

**63:** A casino barge sits on land across highway 90, center, in Biloxi, Miss. Tuesday Aug. 30, 2005 after Hurricane Katrina passed through the area. The barge floated in the Gulf of Mexico, left, and was forced ashore by the onslaught of Katrina.

**64:** Residential homes are shattered north of highway 90, bottom, in Biloxi, Miss., Tuesday, Aug. 30, 2005 after hurricane Katrina passed through the area.

62

*AP Photo/John Bazemore*

63

*AP Photo/Peter Cosgrove*

64

*AP Photo/Spencer Green*

**65:** Lisa Hochstetler with United Canine, a volunteer search group from Ohio, and her dog Grisley search for victims of Hurricane Katrina in East Biloxi, Miss., Tuesday, Sept. 6, 2005.

**66:** The Palace Casino in Biloxi, Miss. partially lies underwater Tuesday Aug. 30, 2005 after Hurricane Katrina passed through the area.

65

*AP Photo/Peter Cosgrove*

66

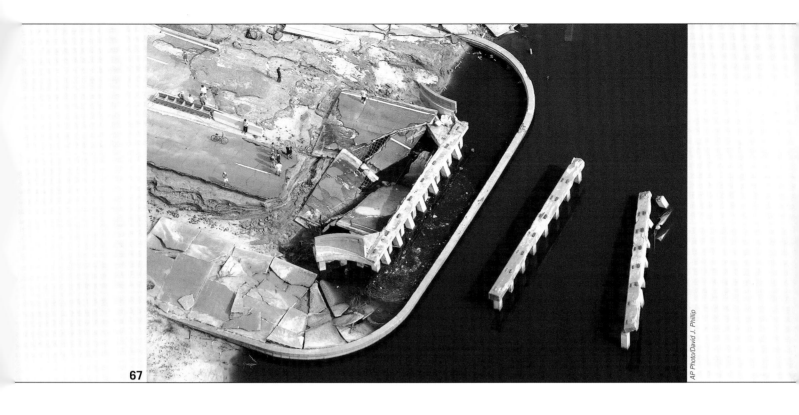

**67**

**67:** People look over a bridge damaged by Hurricane Katrina Wednesday, Aug. 31, 2005 in Bay Saint Louis, Miss.

**68:** A house damaged by Hurricane Katrina burns out of control , Wednesday, Aug. 31, 2005, in Gulfport, Miss.

**68**

69

70

71

**69:** The span of highway 90 leading into in Biloxi, Miss. is totally destroyed Tuesday Aug. 30, 2005 after Hurricane Katrina passed through the area.

**70:** The American flag waves in front of a house destroyed by Hurricane Katrina, Wednesday, Aug. 31, 2005, in Biloxi, Miss.

**71:** Florida Department of Law Enforcement police watch from their all-terrain vehicles as a Navy hovercraft lands on the beach in Gulfport, Miss., on Sunday, Sept. 11, 2005. Members of the Navy have been arriving on a daily basis to help with the clean-up and recovery after Hurricane Katrina hit the area nearly two weeks ago.

AP Photo/David J. Phillips

**77:** Debris from Hurricane Katrina burns in the background of an area damaged by the hurricane Wednesday, Aug. 31, 2005 in Long Beach, Miss.

**78:** Five-year-old Alexes Wizniewski sleeps with her stuffed rabbit in the auditorium of the Gulfport High School in Gulfport, Miss., which served as a shelter for residents who lost their homes in Hurricane Katrina on Thurday, Sept. 8, 2005.

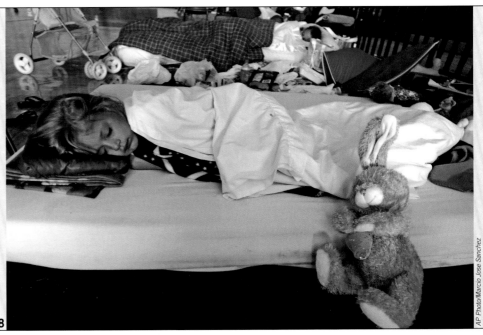

AP Photo/Marcio Jose Sanchez

**80**

**79:** Rhonda Braden walks through the destruction in her childhood neighborhood, Wednesday Aug. 31, 2005 in Long Beach, Miss. Braden was there checking on her father's house that received major water damage from Hurricane Katrina.

**80:** Father Harold Roberts speaks to his congregation during services at the Episcopal Church of the Redeemer, Sunday, Sept. 4, 2005 in Biloxi, Miss. Services were held outdoors on the site of the church that was destroyed by Hurricane Katrina.

**81:** Policemen from the Florida Highway Patrol inspect the damage caused by Hurricane Katrina as they walk down a street in Bay St. Louis, Miss., on Sunday, Sept. 11, 2005.

**81**

# ALABAMA

Although Alabama was spared a direct hit from Katrina, several tornadoes spawned by Katrina caused extensive damage.

82

AP Photo/Rob Carr

83

**84**

**85**

**82:** Water from Hurricane Katrina floods the road leading to the beach in Gulf Shores, Ala., Monday Aug. 29, 2005.

**83:** Boats of all types and sizes sit aground near a waterfront neighborhood in Ocean Springs, Miss., Tuesday, Aug. 30, 2005, following Hurricane Katrina's landfall.

**84:** Remnants of beach houses along Bienville Blvd. on Dauphin Island, Ala., show storm surge damage from Hurricane Katrina's landfall along the Gulf Coast, Tuesday, Aug. 30, 2005.

**85:** An oil platform ripped from its mooring in the Gulf of Mexico rests by the shore in Dauphin Island, Ala. Tuesday Aug. 30, 2005 after Hurricane Katrina passed through the area. The potential damage to oil platforms, refineries and pipelines that remain closed along the Gulf Coast drove energy prices to new highs Tuesday, with crude futures briefly topping $70 a barrel and wholesale gasoline costs surging to levels that lead to $3 and more per gallon at the pump in some markets.

**86:** Churchgoers pray during a National Day of Prayer and Remembrance for victims and survivors of Hurricane Katrina, at the Cathedral of the Immaculate Conception, in Camden, N.J. Friday, Sept. 16, 2005.

86

AP Photo/John David Mercer, Pool

# Hurricane
# RITA

Rita was an intense, destructive and deadly hurricane that significantly impacted the Florida Keys and devastated portions of Southeastern Texas and Southern Louisiana. Rita became a depression just east of the Turks and Caicos Islands late on 17 September. It moved westward and became a tropical storm the following afternoon. Continuing on through the central Bahamas on 19 September, Rita approached hurricane strength with 70 mph winds. While Rita did not strengthen during the following night it rapidly intensified on 20 September while moving through the Florida Straits. It reached category two intensity as the center passed about 50 miles south of Key West. Even though the center did not make landfall in the Florida Keys, it downed trees and produced storm tides of up to five feet in portions of the island chain flooding sections of U.S. Highway 1 and many other streets as well as several homes and businesses.

87

AP Photo/Pat Sullivan

After entering the Gulf of Mexico, Rita intensified at an astounding rate from category two to category five in about 24 hours, with winds reaching 165 mph on the afternoon of 21 September. The hurricane strengthened further and reached a peak intensity of 175 mph early on 22 September about 570 miles east-southeast of Galveston, Texas. The central pressure fell to 897 mb, the third lowest on record in the Atlantic Basin, displacing to fifth lowest, the 902 mb measurement in Hurricane Katrina less than one month earlier. Rita began to weaken later that day, but as it passed through the gulf it produced storm surge flooding in portions of the New Orleans area that had previously been inundated by Katrina. Rita turned Northwestward and weakened to category three on 23 September. It then made landfall around 2:30 a.m. CDT, 24 September just east of the Texas/Louisiana border between Sabine Pass and Johnston's Bayou still at category three intensity with 120 mph winds.

Rita caused devastating storm surge flooding and wind damage in Southwestern Louisiana and extreme Southeastern Texas. It weakened after moving inland, but remained a tropical storm until reaching Northwestern Louisiana late on 24 September. It then turned Northeastward and merged with a frontal system two days later.

88

AP Photo/Matt Slocum

**87:** Cars are bumper to bumper on Interstate-45 near downtown Houston in anticipation of Hurricane Rita Thursday, Sept. 22, 2005. Thousands of people evacuated the Texas coast and officials reversed the Southbound lane on the interstate to four lanes of north bound flow.

**88:** Emergency crews investigate the scene where a bus caught fire and exploded on northbound Interstate 45, Friday, Sept. 23, in Wilmer, Texas. The bus carrying elderly evacuees from Hurricane Rita caught fire and was rocked by explosions early Friday on a gridlocked highway near Dallas, killing as many as 24 people, authorities said. The bus, with about 45 people on board, had been traveling since Thursday.

**89:** A refinery in Baytown, Texas, is shown in this aerial view after Hurricane Rita made landfall Saturday, Sept. 24, 2005.

89

AP Photo/David J. Phillip

**90:** The site where homes once stood in Holly Beach, is shown in this aerial view in the aftermath of Hurricane Rita Sunday, Sept. 25, 2005 in Cameron Parish, La.

**91:** The devastated lower Ninth Ward district of New Orleans is still flooded Sunday, Sept. 25, 2005, after Hurricane Rita swept through the area on Saturday. The storm surge created by Hurricane Rita eroded repairs made after Katrina and sent water surging back into the already devastated Ninth Ward.

# REFLECTION

_____

_____

_____

_____

_____

_____

_____

_____

_____

_____

_____

_____

_____

_____

_____

_____

_____